FOLK-TALES
FROM GREECE
I

to my sister Artemis
M.S.

FOLK-TALES
FROM GREECE
I

Retold by Menelaos Stephanides
Illustrated by Photini Stephanidi

Translation
Bruce Walter

☙

SIGMA

FOLK-TALES FROM GREECE: **I**

ISBN: 960-425-082-5

© 2002 Sigma Publications
Second run 2004
These stories are original versions and neither text nor
illustrations may be reproduced in any form without
the written permission of the copyright holders.

Published and printed in Greece

20, Mavromihali Street, tel. +30 210 3607667, fax +30 210 3638941
GR-106 80 ATHENS
www.sigmabooks.gr   e-mail: sigma@sigmabooks.gr

CONTENTS

The Water-nymph
and the Veil

randpa, tell us the story about the water nymph and the veil!"

"But I've told you that tale so many times already. Don't tell me you want it yet again?"

"We like it, grandpa, because it's true."

"And it's different from all the other stories."

"And it says we had a great, great grandmother who was a water nymph."

"A water nymph for a grandmother! But that was two hundred years ago – maybe four hundred, even. Even so, it's just a fairy story, children, like all the others. But let's hear it once again, since that is what you want so much – and I shall tell it exactly as our own grandmother used to, when we were children just like you.

Well now, in those years long gone, when water nymphs came out at dusk along the rivers, there lived here in this very village a great, great, great grandfather of yours – yes, right here in this house, although it wasn't as it is today, for it was burned down in the wars.

Now don't imagine this grandfather of yours as a bent old man, dragging himself along with a walking-stick. Like all grandfathers, he was a young man once, and a handsome, daring fellow, too. Why, the pride of all the village, he was!

One day, this brave young grandfather of yours set off for a wedding which was being held in a neighbouring village, lower down the mountain.

On leaving the house, he swung his shotgun over

his shoulder, as all the menfolk did in those days, for it was only by force of arms that we could keep our villages free in those distant years.

The wedding feast lasted three whole days and nights – and don't forget your grandfather was no old doddering grandpa then. He ate and drank and sang and danced as if he'd never stop, and it was only when the third night was drawing towards dawn that he set off on the journey home.

To make a shorter walk of it, he took a short cut through the olive grove which stands on the plateau between the villages. The first grey light of dawn was slowly creeping into the night sky, when in the morning silence he heard the distant sound of girls' happy voices, and snatches of sweet song. The young man stood there trying to hear more clearly and soon the sounds came closer, till in a while he saw a group of water nymphs approaching through the olive trees. When they were quite close by, they all joined hands and started dancing in a ring. They were dressed in robes of finest gossamer, spun from a million spiders' webs and bright with all the colours of the rainbow, and they held long veils which floated light as thistledown in the still morning air.

When they caught sight of your grandfather, they showed no trace of fear. Instead, the leader of the dance, a lovely water nymph with golden hair and eyes as blue as cornflowers, stepped close to the confused young fellow, took him by the hand and drew him into the ring of dancers. So he could perform more freely in the centre of the circle, she gave him one end of her veil to hold. Hesitantly at first, but then with growing courage, the young man threw himself into the swirling rhythm, delighted by the fair and laughing maidens all around him, and most of all by the water nymph who had held out her hand to him and whom he now held by the trailing end of her long veil. The laughter and the whirling

15

dance were at their height when suddenly a water nymph cried out:

"The sun! The sun! The sun is coming up!"

"The sun! The sun!" echoed the other nymphs in horror, and unclasping their hands, they raised them high above their hands, spun round upon their toes and disappeared into thin air! But the nymph who had drawn him into the dance was forced to stay behind, since he still grasped her firmly by the end of her veil. There was a look of terror and bewilderment upon her face, for while she should have faded into morning mist like all the others, there she was still standing next to the young man. She soon realised it was the veil he held which kept her there, and she gave it a quick, desperate tug to free herself and disappear like her companions. But your grandfather knew all too well just what would happen if he loosed his grip, so he held on tighter still and would not let her take the veil. With tears of des-

16

peration in her eyes, the water nymph begged him to let her have it back, but the young man, who all this while was gazing into her deep blue eyes as if bewitched, had no intention of letting her take her veil from him. Instead, he gave it such a violent tug that the veil slipped from her grasp.

"My veil! My veil! You must give me my veil again, so I can join my sisters!" cried the nymph in alarm. But the young man did nothing of the sort – instead of giving it back to her, he thrust it quickly down the barrel of his shotgun!

"Now take it, if you can!" he told her, swinging the barrel round in her direction.

"Of course I can," replied the nymph in a determined voice, stretching out her hand to snatch the veil back.

But as she did so, she recoiled as if she had been struck. It was the fumes of the gunpowder which still clung to the barrel of the shotgun, a smell which water nymphs find hateful beyond bearing. She tried again, but again her hand sprang back as if it had been slapped, so horrible was the smell to her.

In despair, she begged the young man once again to give her back her veil, but he replied:

"Listen, lovely maiden. I did not take your veil because I wish you harm, but because I love you and want you to stay with me for ever. Come away with me, and I shall make you happy."

"But can a water nymph ever be happy living among mortals? Don't you understand?" the girl protested.

"Yet I cannot give you up. That is something you must understand as well. You have given me my happiness, and I will not let you take it back from me."

"But I must, I must!" cried out the nymph, and she leapt to pull away the veil. Her fingers had almost closed around the delicately woven fabric when the acrid stench of the gunpowder struck her nostrils with such violence that she almost fell senseless to the ground.

Knowing she was defeated, the water nymph looked the young man in the eyes and said:

"I know that I have no choice but to follow you. I believe that you will treat me kindly, but nothing will ever soften the pain of losing my freedom. And I warn you that a day shall come when you will give back my veil and let me go; but that will only happen when you have learned to love me more deeply than any man has ever loved before, for only then will you have it in your heart to feel true pity for me. Now let us go."

Delighted that he had at last persuaded the nymph to come with him, your grandfather said nothing in reply except,

"There is one other thing I want from you: tell me your name. Mine is Alexis."

The water nymph, however, gave no answer. The

young man understood: nymphs never reveal their name to mortals.

"Let's go then...... Katerina," said Alexis in the end. And he took her by the hand.

She did not pull it back, and hearing the name that he had given her, she gave a smile, although it was a bitter one. From that day on, her whole life would be changed. From being a water nymph, she would become the wife of this young man. Yet how could she forget the joyful, carefree existence she had once led with her sisters, along the river banks and in the forests, by the pale light of the moon? That is why she followed the happy young man with dragging footsteps and sad, downcast eyes.

The water nymph married her captor. Alexis and Katerina seemed a well-matched couple, for your grandfather showered his bride with such love and tenderness that all the world was sure she must be happy. But no, just as a bird you take away from

the forest and imprison in a cage will always long to regain its freedom, however much loving care you lavish on it, so Katerina longed to take her veil back and be reunited with her sisters. Yet the hideous stench of the gunpowder always held her in check and so she stifled her yearning to be once more with the other water nymphs among the rivers and the forests of her home.

The years rolled by. Katerina and Alexis had children and both loved them deeply. Alexis had hoped that once the young ones came, Katerina would decide to stay for ever with her human family. But it was not to be. Much as she adored her babies, a smile never crossed her lips again, and her longing to be back with her sisters did not fade away. Instead, as time went past, it grew even greater still – so great that it became a leaden burden weighing on her heart. Your grandfather could see all this and pitied her. He was as kind and tender to her as it was in his power to be, yet he saw that all his efforts were in vain, and many times he told himself the time had come to give her back her veil and set her free. Each time, however, the knowledge that this would leave their children without a mother's care was enough to give him second thoughts. But eventually a time arrived when his pity for the mother overcame his anguish for their young ones, and then he recalled the words his wife the water nymph had spoken all those years ago:

"A day shall come when you will give me back my veil and let me go; but that will only happen when you have come to love me more deeply than any man has ever loved before."

"And now that day has come," thought Alexis. And with a heavy heart he went and pulled the veil from the barrel of the gun and returned it to her.

It was in the grey light before dawn, and the sun had not yet risen over the horizon, when the water nymph took back her veil. With mixed feelings of joy and sorrow, she kissed her husband, quickly did the housework, prepared the children's morning meal, and, as the first rays of the sun bathed the mountain tops with rosy light, she ran and kissed the youngsters as they slept. Then, with a final gesture of farewell to her husband, she suddenly became thin air and vanished.

Your grandmother the water nymph had gone for ever. Yet every morning, your grandfather's house was clean-swept and tidy, the midday meal was simmering in the pot, and breakfast would lie waiting on the table. Every day it was the same, until the children had grown up and your grandfather Alexis, a real grandfather by now, had closed his eyes for ever.

That, children, is the tale of the water nymph and the veil. And whenever my own grandmother told it to us, she would say at the end, in a voice which

showed that she believed it, every single word: 'And so, children, since your grandmother was a water nymph, you have the blood of water-nymphs your-selves.'

And that's what I must tell you now: 'You have the blood of water nymphs in you' – if the tale is true, that is.

"It is true, grandpa!"

"True!"

"True!"

"It is true!"

The Soothsayer

Once upon a time, in a distant kingdom, there lived a lazy fellow called Cicada. All day long his wife Hazel kept on scolding him because he wouldn't go out to work and there was nothing for them to eat.

"Go and be a labourer," she would tell him.

"That's not the kind of work for me," he'd answer.

"Then be a builder," she would say.

"That's not my sort of job," Cicada always repeated.

"Become a blacksmith, then – make horseshoes."

But idle Cicada would usually give the same reply:

"Those aren't the kind of jobs for me."

Another time, still yawning lazily, he came out with these words: "Just you wait and see. One day this husband of yours will be a minister of the king."

"You could be right at that," said Hazel with a mocking laugh. "In this kingdom it's fellows like you who get the high positions. And come to think of it, I'd rather like to be a minister's fine lady."

"No, I'll settle down and become a blacksmith after all, ha! ha!" laughed lazy Cicada. And so the time went by and he did nothing whatsoever.

One lunchtime, as he was making his way back home and wondering if there would be anything in the house for him to eat, he heard the next door neighbour shrieking that thieves had run off with her hen.

"A curse on him, whoever took it!" she kept crying, making enough noise with her wails to wake the dead.

29

"Hey, why all this fuss about a single hen?" Cicada asked her. And just so he wouldn't have to listen to her screaming any more, he added:

"It's fallen down the well. Drop a bucket down and pull it out. But if you find it, you will give me something for my trouble, all right?"

The neighbour ran to the well, dropped the bucket in, and when she hauled it up again, there was the hen inside, a little bedraggled, but safe and sound!

She gave a penny to Cicada, and he ran straight to his wife shouting, "Look what I've got in my hand! Off you go to get some bread for us to eat and then I'll tell you the funny thing that happened."

Hazel ran straight off to the baker's and they wolfed down the loaf the moment she got back. Then Cicada told her how he'd come to earn it.

Hazel listened open-mouthed.

"That's it!" she cried, once he had finished. "You can become a magician – a soothsayer!"

30

"Hm, not a bad idea at that. It rather suits me, come to think of it. But just how does one become a soothsayer? I don't know anything about telling fortunes."

"You don't have to know," replied his wife. "If others have done it, so can you. All you've got to do is look the part and put a bold face on it."

So they rummaged in an old chest, fitted Cicada out in an assortment of brightly-coloured robes, and he became a soothsayer.

The news soon spread throughout the kingdom, and one day there arrived at Cicada's door some men sent by the king to learn if the child the queen was going to bear would be a boy or girl.

They were the very last people our magician wanted to set eyes on.

"How do you expect me to put a bold face on it now?" he muttered to Hazel.

"What did you say?" the king's men asked him.

"Oh, nothing, nothing," he replied. But they pressed him to reply:

"Won't you tell us what child the queen is going to bear, great soothsayer?"

Cicada was even more terrified by now, and he began to say:

"A boy, a girl, a boy, a girl, a boy, a girl ..."

The king's men saw that they weren't going to get any sense out of him, so they gave up and left.

Shortly after this, the queen gave birth – and she had not one baby but twins: a boy and a girl.

"Your majesty!" the courtiers said in surprise. "The soothsayer was right. He told us the queen would bear you a boy and a girl. He is a true magician, after all." And the king did not forget this.

A few days later, the king's golden casket filled with sovereigns disappeared from the palace.

They searched the kingdom from end to end, but it was nowhere to be found.

Then the king ordered, "Bring the soothsayer to me."

Cicada was led into the royal presence with a fanfare of trumpets and the king ordered him to go and find the golden casket.

At these words, panic seized the false magician (as if there are any real ones!). But to hide his confusion, and because he was hungry, too, he asked,

"Give me a few hazelnuts and a drop of brandy wine."

"What on earth can he want them for?" the courtiers whispered among themselves.

"He is a magician," replied the king, "and he will know."

The soothsayer took the hazelnuts and the brandy and set off filled with dread. On his way, he ate a few of the nuts and told himself,

"A little nap would do me good."

These words were hardly out of Cicada's mouth

when he spotted a deserted hut. And who should be sitting in it but the thieves who had robbed the king! As soon as they spotted him, they took to their heels and hid themselves. Once our magician was in the hut, he ate a few more of the nuts and drank a little of the brandy. Then he lay down on the floor and murmured, "Here comes the first one," and with a single great yawn he fell fast asleep.

What he meant was the first yawn – but one of the thieves had crept up to the door to listen, and when he heard the magician's words he fled in terror to the others and gasped,

"He knew I was there! As soon as I put my ear to the door, do you know what he said? 'Here comes the first one'. He must be a magician!"

Not long after this, the soothsayer woke up, ate a few more of the hazelnuts, took another pull at the brandy bottle and felt sleepy once again.

"Here comes the second," he said, as he yawned

once more and closed his eyes.

And would you believe it — at that very moment the second thief had put his ear to the door!

"He knew I was there, too!" he ran to tell his companions, trembling with fear. "As soon as I bent down, he said, 'Here comes the second'!"

"Well, then it's my turn to go," the third thief said, but he wrapped his scarf around his head because he was afraid that the magician might recognize him.

Meanwhile, Cicada had woken up, eaten a few more of the nuts and drunk a drop or two of brandy. Sure enough, he soon felt sleepy again, but by now he was rather cold as well, so wrapping his robe around himself for warmth, he lay down for the third time and, as another great yawn escaped him, he murmured, "Here comes the third one, all wrapped up!" and fell asleep.

Scared out of his wits, the listening thief ran

straight back to the others and told them,

"All is lost! As soon as I got near, he said, 'Here comes the third one, all wrapped up'!"

By now the three thieves were in despair. And being stupid, as all thieves are, they went into the hut, woke Cicada up and told him:

"We know you have recognized us for the thieves who robbed the king. If you promise not to tell on us and let us get away, we'll tell you where we've hidden the casket."

"Done!" cried the soothsayer, rubbing his hands with glee.

"It's just here. Dig and you will find it," the thieves told him.

Then the magician went and brought two soldiers. They did the digging, because Cicada, as we have seen, was a lazy fellow, and when they had got the casket up, the three of them set off for the palace.

When the golden treasure chest was opened in the

presence of the king, it was filled to the brim. Not a single sovereign was missing. The king was overwhelmed with joy and placed the soothsayer beside him at the royal table. When they had eaten and drunk their fill, they went out in the garden for a stroll.

As they wandered under the trees, the king quickly plucked a cicada from a hazel bush while the soothsayer was not looking, and hid it in his fist.

"There is one more question I shall put to you," he said, "to see how great a magician you really are. I want you to guess what I am holding in my hand."

"Oh, what have I got myself into?" groaned Cicada under his breath. "My wife Hazel is to blame for everything!" Then he spoke to himself aloud, in a despairing voice:

"It's your own fault, Cicada. You shouldn't have let that Hazel deliver you into the king's hands!"

The king, of course, thought that Cicada was talk-

ing about the little insect he had picked from off the hazel bush and held hidden in his fist. He was convinced by now that this was no ordinary magician. And so he placed both lazy Cicada and his Hazel among his ministers at court. For that is how ministers were created once upon a time.

Beauty and the Swan

Once upon a time, there lived a nobleman and a miller who had been great friends for years. They married on the same day, and took two wives who were themselves inseparable friends. Indeed, they all lived so happily together they gave their word that if they happened to have children, they, too, would marry one another.

Some time later, the nobleman's wife gave birth to a lovely baby girl. When she was a little older they named her Beauty, for there was not a lovelier creature in the world.

On the same day that the girl was born, the miller's wife also had a baby. But, as sometimes happens in fairy tales, she gave birth to – a bird! A bird with a long neck which grew up into a swan – a fair white swan with a human voice.

Beauty adored the swan and would play with it all day, for the families' two houses stood side by side.

It was impossible to keep any secrets when they were such close neighbours, and so one day Beauty and the swan learned of the vow their parents had made before their birth. Not long after this, the swan told his father to go to the nobleman and remind him of the promise he had given all those years before.

So the miller went to Beauty's father and told him,

"Our children have grown up, and the time has come to marry them, as we agreed when we were newly-wed."

When he heard this, the nobleman was filled with sadness.

"Why are you looking so downcast, my dear?" his wife asked him that evening.

"I'm at my wits' end, wife," he answered. "The miller came today and told me that the time has come to marry Beauty to that swan of theirs."

As soon as she heard this, his wife burst out laughing.

"Is that all you're looking so miserable about, husband? Leave it to me. I'll go and see the miller's wife and no more will be said about it."

But when she went, the miller's wife reminded her,

"We gave our word before the picture of the Holy Virgin. Do you want God to send his fire down upon us?"

And so Beauty and the swan were married.

But as the joyful wedding feast went on around

them, the mother of the bride wept tears which nobody could comfort and her father sat hunched in silence, his drooping head clutched in his hands.

That evening, when the song and dance were over and everyone had staggered home to bed, the bride and groom withdrew into their chamber and there a miracle occurred! The swan spread wide his great broad wings and was instantly transformed into a handsome youth.

"Yes, I am your husband," he told the startled girl. "Now listen to me carefully. Every evening, when we close our chamber door behind us, I shall become a man; and in the morning, before we open it again, I shall turn back into a swan. And if you speak of this to nobody, then in fifteen days I shall become a man for good. But should you reveal this secret to any living soul, then I shall be lost to you for ever and you will never set eyes on me again. Alas, that is the fortune which the cruel Fates have written for me."

Beauty was beside herself with joy. She almost ran to her mother there and then, to tell her that the swan was really a young man – and the most handsome in the world, at that. But she held herself in check and asked,

"Can I not even tell my mother?"

"Are you mad? You can tell nobody – nobody, I say – if you do not wish to lose me."

"It's only fifteen days," thought Beauty. "They will pass." And she patiently kept her secret to herself.

Meanwhile, however, Beauty's mother had fallen sick with grief. However good and kind the swan might be, and however much her daughter loved him, there was no denying that he was not a man. And by the fourteenth day she had become so ill that Beauty feared that she might die. So she bent down to her mother's ear and quietly, very quietly, whispered her secret, adding that next day the fifteen days would end and the swan become a man for ever.

Beauty's poor mother was so overjoyed that the sickness left her in a flash. But when they ran to find the swan, it was nowhere to be found. Her father joined them and they searched both high and low, but all in vain. Exactly what the swan had warned had happened.

Then Beauty told her parents, "You know how much I love you and I know the love you feel for me, but do not deny me the favour I'm going to ask you. Give me three pairs of iron-shod shoes and a purse full of gold sovereigns. Give me your blessing, too, and I will search the whole world over, to find my man and bring him home again."

"But my child, the world is boundless," said her father. "Where will you begin your search, and where do you think it will end? Stay here, child – let us not lose you as well."

Beauty begged them every day, however, and seeing that they had no choice her parents gave her

what she wanted and bade a sad farewell.

Beauty set off for distant lands. She knocked on every door and asked – sometimes about a fair white swan and at others for news of the most handsome young man in the world. But nobody knew who or what the girl was talking of. She met witches, talked with water-nymphs and sought the counsel of wise men, but nobody could tell her anything. A year went by and her first pair of iron-shod shoes had worn to holes, and all she learned was that another fair young man, who had been a swan before, had also made a sudden disappearance and not been heard of since. A second year passed, and another pair of iron shoes wore out, and again, the only news which reached her ears was that a third young man, who had also been born as a swan, had disappeared just like her husband.

So she would not wear out the third pair of iron shoes, Beauty stopped walking and opened an inn at a crossroads where many travellers passed. She would accept no money from those who came to spend the night, but only begged them to repeat the most fantastic stories that they knew.

A whole year had gone by, when two beggars arrived at the inn, one lame and one blind. She gave them a hot meal and invited them to stay and spend the night.

"Just tell me the strangest story you have ever heard," she asked them.

"We've got a tale to tell you," said the lame beggar. "It's true, but yet so very strange you won't believe a word of it. No matter – here it is:

Yesterday, in the morning, when we were coming here, we sat down on a river bank to eat a few dried crusts of bread and rest our weary legs. I bent over to soak the hard scraps in the water and make them soft enough to eat, but it seems that I was careless, for the current carried them away. I ran downstream to fish them out again, but as I'm lame I couldn't keep up with the swiftly-flowing water. However, in my efforts I went on quite a way and reached a place where rocks had made a little waterfall. There were some steps beside it. I hobbled down them and then I saw a great door in the rock. I opened it and found myself in a corridor cut in the stone.

Filled with curiosity, I went on further, until I came to a bake-oven – and what I saw next was simply unbelievable. There before my eyes was a wooden shovel, lifting the baked loaves from the oven all by itself! I reached out to take one and the shovel gave me a sharp blow on the wrist. And that wasn't all – it spoke to me as well!

'Let the young masters eat first!' it told me.

I went on further down and came upon a kitchen, with hot food simmering in the cooking pots. I made as if to taste some – and up sprang a ladle and rapped me on the knuckles. You could have knocked me down with a feather!

'Wait till my masters have had their fill!' it snapped at me.

I went on further still and found myself in a vast chamber with a lovely carved stone pool in which the waters of the river flowed. I gazed around me in amazement. The walls were clad in marble, there were tall, wide doors and windows, and crystal mirrors threw back the dancing flames from the splendid fireplace in the corner. I saw a great round table spread with food before me, and I could see it had been set for three. There were three chairs as well. Everything there was rich and good enough for lords. It was a real palace. Suddenly three swans came sailing into the pool. I ran to hide behind the door and spied on them. The swans reached the lip of the pool and started to climb out of the water. But the moment they set foot on the ground, all three of them turned into handsome young men."

When Beauty heard how the swans had been transformed, she immediately jumped to her feet.

"Can you take me to the place?" she asked him anxiously.

"Well, yes, I can. But let me finish first."

"Let's go!" she said. "You can tell me on the way." And she pulled him from his chair and off they went.

They reached the river and went on to the waterfall. Beauty saw the door and opened it.

"From here on I shall go alone," she said. "Here, take these sovereigns and the key to the inn door. From now on, you can keep it with your blind friend and you'll never have to beg again. Good luck to the pair of you."

So she went on alone, and soon she reached the bake-oven.

"Good morning to you, Mistress Beauty!" the shovel greeted her.

"Good morning to you, Mistress Beauty!" cried the ladle as she went into the kitchen.

"It's Beauty, it's Beauty! Our lady Beauty has arrived at last!" called all the doors and windows as she reached the splendid chamber. Beauty stood there on the threshold, her eyes glistening with tears of joy.

And lo and behold, the three swans came sailing in once more. She immediately hid behind a door and watched in astonishment as the great birds left the water and were transformed upon the instant into men. All that was left upon the lip of the stone pool was their broad white wings. Beauty recognized her husband straight away. He was clad in robes of gold, like a king's son, as were the other handsome youths, but the faces of all three were pale with grief.

They went and sat down at the table spread with food. One of the young men raised his glass and said,

"I drink to the health of my beloved, who couldn't

keep our secret three more days. Weep, friends! Weep, doors and windows!"

All three broke into sobs, and the doors and windows joined them.

Then the second young man raised his glass and said,

"To the health of my dear bride, who couldn't keep our secret two more days. Weep, friends! Weep doors and windows!"

And once again the three fair youths broke into sobs, and the doors and windows joined them.

Then the third youth raised his glass in turn.

"To the health of my dear Beauty, who couldn't keep our secret one more day. Weep, friends! Weep, doors and windows!"

The three youths wept afresh, but the doors and windows laughed instead!

"Weep, doors! Weep, windows!" the young man shouted angrily.

But they laughed louder still. And the loudest laughs of all came from the door his wife was hidden behind.

This made the young man angrier yet, and he leapt to his feet to smash the door down with his fists. But as he did so, Beauty sprang out from behind and fell into his arms. And there they stood for a long moment, weeping tears of joy.

Suddenly a thought flashed into Beauty's head. She broke away from him, picked up the swans' wings which lay by the pool side and flung them all into the fire.

"You have saved us!" the three handsome youths cried in delight. "We shall never be transformed into swans again."

"And now let us go home to our parents," Beauty told her husband. "They will not believe it when they see us once again. Three whole years we have been lost to them."

"We shall leave here, too, and both of us will find our brides again," added the other two young men. And they all went up into the sunlight. There, by the waterfall, three white horses waited for them. The other two mounted theirs and Beauty climbed up with her husband on the third. They exchanged a fond farewell and then all went their separate ways.

Long though their journey was, their white horse made short work of it, and soon the young couple were in their parents' arms again. Tears of happiness washed away all memory of the years of anguished waiting. A great feast of welcome was laid on and it lasted a whole month. But I was not among the guests — and would you believe me if I said I had been?

The Sad Nightingale

Once upon a time there lived a king and queen who had two children. One was a gentle girl, all freshness and grace, and the other a good-hearted, handsome little boy.

Nothing could keep the two apart, so deep was their love for one another, and their parents adored them for their kind hearts, their good looks and their charm, especially the girl, whose beauty dazzled everyone who saw her.

This fair princess was only twelve years old, still a mere child, and yet she was the talk of all the world, from North to South and from East to West. 'The loveliest maid on earth', they called her.

Noble young men, rich sons of lords and famous princes were already coming from every corner of the world to seek the lovely maiden's hand, but she had no desire to be married off so young. She did not want to be parted from her parents and the little brother who was the great love of her life. And besides, she was so happy as she was!

Yet happiness is like a bird of passage, soon to fly away, while misery is always with us, waiting its chance to strike.

One morning, the two youngsters were in the palace garden as usual, happily skipping and dancing. The beautiful maiden had taken off her headscarf, a white silk square embroidered all around with scarlet roses, and as she danced she waved it in the air. But suddenly a gust of wind whirled up around her, plucked the scarf from her fingers, lifted it high in the sky, then blew it down behind

some bushes. The little boy ran off at once to find it. He burrowed his way into the thick foliage while the girl waited for him to bring the headscarf back. He was gone for a long time, and his worried sister went to see what could be keeping him. There was no sign of the lad. She called and called but got no answer, and there was no sign of the headscarf either. The princess ran here and there, anxiously crying out his name, but there was no reply. All she heard was a nightingale, whose sad voice seemed to be trying to answer her shrill calls, and nothing more. A few moments later, the bird's song grew more distant and faded into silence. As for her brother, he had completely disappeared. Days went by, then months, and no one knew whether the boy was still alive or dead.

Nothing could console the king and queen for the loss of their dear son, while for the princess it was even worse. She missed him more than she could bear. No longer did she play or laugh, but thought only of her brother and the sad cry of the nightingale.

A whole year passed, and by now the king and queen had accepted their son's loss. But his sister was as pale and miserable as ever.

"Losing one child was bad enough," her unfortunate parents said. "If this goes on, we'll lose the other, too." And not knowing what else to suggest, they urged her to marry one of the many fine young men who came to seek her hand. But the girl would not even hear of marrying. Her only thoughts were of the little brother who had gone from her, and the only voice she heard was the sad cry of the nightingale.

"What ails you, child?" her father asked one day, seeing the tears which trickled down her cheeks. "Tell us what can bring a smile back to your lips."

And then, in a voice so low he strained to catch

the words, the princess told him, "I want to see the sad nightingale."

"The poor girl's lost her mind," the king muttered. "What is this sad nightingale she speaks of, and where can it be found?"

Three days afterwards, he asked her the same question and she answered as before. And when another two days had gone by, and he could not stop himself from asking yet again, she answered with the same strange words: "I want to see the sad nightingale." At this, the king proclaimed that he would give his daughter's hand in marriage to whatever young man could make her wish come true and cure her of her terrible unhappiness.

The very next day, the royal heralds went round the towns and villages of the kingdom, proclaiming that the loveliest maiden in the world would become the bride of the man who brought her the sad nightingale.

65

The news spread far and wide, and many a bold young fellow set out on the endeavour. There were princes riding in golden coaches with armies of attendants, rich young noblemen on horseback and countless other daring youths, each believing that he would be the one to find the sad nightingale and marry the beautiful princess.

The king's word also reached the house of a rich merchant. This man had a son whom everyone called Snooty, because he was ridiculously proud. But the merchant also had an apprentice, younger than his son, an orphaned lad who was good-hearted and hardworking.

Snooty asked his father for a horse, a birdcage and a purse full of gold florins, and set off like the others, his head filled with dreams of how he would become a prince and —why not?— even king one day.

The young apprentice also had his dreams, but

they were very different. When he thought of the princess, all he saw was a young girl grieving over her lost brother, and that is why he asked his master to let him go as well, in search of the sad nightingale.

"How far can the fellow get? He'll be back soon enough," the merchant told himself, and so he gave him leave to try. All he gave the apprentice for the journey was a bag of bread and cheese, but the lad took a pair of scissors with him, too. These scissors were the only thing he owned, and had been left him by his mother.

Snooty, who had set off first, soon reached a crossroads, where he found an old woman dressed in rags sitting on a stone. She was skinny and wrinkled and shivering from head to toe. She wore no shoes and sat with one leg resting on the other, holding her bare foot in both hands and moaning. As Snooty rode up to her she cried,

"Help me, young man! I am in pain. Help me, and

you shall have my blessing!"

"I never saw such a hideous old creature," said Snooty to himself and then, out loud, he sneered, "Help you, old woman? You look past help to me!" And with these words he set the spurs to his horse and galloped away, quite deaf to the shower of curses she sent after him.

Some time later, the apprentice passed by the same spot. He saw the sorry state the poor old woman was in and immediately took pity on her. Without waiting to be asked, he went to her side, enquired why she was moaning and asked if he could be of any help.

"May good fortune bless your footsteps, kind young man!" the old crone cried. "A thorn is buried in my heel, and I cannot see to pull it out."

Gently lifting her foot, the boy found the thorn and drew it out, and immediately the pain went away. Looking kindly at her rescuer, the old woman said,

"Thank you for helping me, my lad. A lot of fine young men have passed this way – nobles and even princes, too. But not one of them would stop to draw the thorn and ease my pain. Had they done so, I would have helped them in my turn if they had any need of it. For there are many things I know, secrets no other person in the world has knowledge of. Now, tell me where you are headed for, and the reason why you are travelling the roads on foot. Do not look at me so doubtfully, for I may prove more useful to you than you could ever imagine."

Although the apprentice did not believe that this poor, distressed old woman could give him any help, he did not want to hurt her feelings by remaining silent.

"I want to bring a smile back to the face of the loveliest maiden in the world," he said, "but that I can only do if I find the sad nightingale and take it to her. Yet no one knows where the bird is to

be found, and I'm sure that you don't either, grand-mother."

"Ah, but I do know, lad," came the reply. "So listen to what I have to tell you. The sad nightingale is to be found beyond the Lofty Mountains. They are too high and far for human feet to reach, but you have a kind heart and if you are as clever and daring as you look, you will overcome all obstacles, find the nightingale you seek, make the lovely princess well again and take her as your bride. Do you see that mountain on the far horizon? You must somehow climb it. But when you reach its summit you will face another mountain. That, too, you must climb. Then there will be another, and another. When you have climbed six mountains, you will reach a seventh, the Untrodden Peak. Whoever sets eyes on that looming tower of rock gives up and turns back in despair, for it is so tall and vast that no one can cross over it. But you must grit your teeth and keep on up as if you

wished to reach its highest crag. On your way, you will come across a cave. The Hairy Giant lives there, a creature who is sometimes wicked but sometimes kind, sometimes savage but sometimes gentle as a lamb. If you can make a good impression on him, he will tell you how to reach the other side of the Untrodden Peak and find the nightingale you seek – but if you fail to win him over, you are done for. I give you my blessing and am sure you will succeed, for my blessing has never failed a person yet. Very few have ever had it, though, for I give it only once in every hundred years. Go on your way now – and may the bag you carry on your shoulder never empty till you are safely back again."

And the moment the last word had left her lips, the old woman turned to air and vanished.

The boy stood gaping at the spot where she had been. But at least he now knew which way he should go, and so he boldly set off for the Lofty Mountains. He walked for days, and the days turned into months. Whenever he felt hungry, he would open his bag and take a bite of bread and cheese, and as the old woman had foretold, the bag never grew empty. Whenever he was thirsty, he would drink from the springs he found along his way, rest for a while and then keep on upwards. He climbed the first mountain and then the second, always moving closer to his goal.

At last he crossed the first six mountains and found himself before the seventh: the Untrodden Peak. It was a towering rocky mass, so tall and broad that it blocked his way like a huge wall. The young man set his sights boldly on the highest pinnacle and began to climb its rocky slopes. Up and up he went, till in the end he spied the cave which the old woman had told him of. He approached it cautiously, peered in and saw the giant.

The giant was the hairiest creature the lad had ever

74

seen. He was sitting cross-legged on the floor of the cave, naked to the waist. His chest was a tangled forest of curly hair which sprouted up to cover his shoulders and spread right down his arms to his fingertips. His bushy beard and his even wilder mat of hair hid all his face except the nose and a little patch of forehead. As for his eyes, they could not be seen at all, for a pair of huge and bristly eyebrows hung over them like a thick curtain. All that stood out in this wild, hairy thicket was a great gold key which hung on a leather cord around his neck and rested on the dark fur of his chest.

Anyone else who set eyes on this fearsome giant would have turned and fled in terror, but the young man stood his ground, quite unafraid. And it soon dawned on him that the giant could not see, for he held his head stiff and unmoving, just as a blind man does.

"Long life and happiness to you, giant," the lad

called out. "I have come to be of service to you. Ask anything you want, and I am yours to command."

"Who are you to come unasked into my home?" the giant roared, stretching out his great hairy arms to seize his unwelcome visitor, but not quick enough to catch the apprentice, who jumped nimbly to one side.

Then, going up to the giant again, he said, "I've come to help you, not to do you harm. That's why I tell you, ask anything you want, and I shall see to it. But afterwards I shall ask a favour of you in my turn, and you must keep your side of the bargain."

"Anything I want?" replied the giant gruffly, "Why, what else would a blind man want but to have his eyesight back again? Can you do that for me? Of course you can't! So get out of here right now if you want to save your skin!"

"And I tell you that I can!" replied the lad, and pulling his mother's scissors from his pocket he trimmed

the giant's eyebrows in a trice. It was as simple as that! The Hairy Giant could see again.

"Well, would you believe it? A mere boy, not even half my size, and he gives me back my sight," the giant chuckled, delighted he could see again at last. "Come on, then, ask me any favour you like and I will do it for you, mark my word. You certainly deserve it!"

"Yes, I have a great favour to ask," replied the lad. "I want you to tell me how I can find the sad nightingale."

"I'll tell you, brave young fellow," said the giant, lifting off the key which hung around his neck. "Here, take this key, and take this hair as well." And he plucked a hair from his long beard and gave it to the lad. "Climb up the steps you'll find at the back of the cave, and keep straight on until you reach an iron door. Unlock it with that key I've given you and you'll come out onto a wide ledge high up on the

77

mountainside. There you must set fire to the hair, and everything will turn out as you wish."

With the key and the long strand of hair clutched tightly in one hand, the boy climbed up the steps the giant had pointed out: great rough-hewn slabs of rock which led him to a long and narrow tunnel, winding up like a snake through the stone heart of the mountain. A feeble glow from some hidden source threw its faint light on rocks of many colours and age-old stalactites. Enchanted by this weird beauty which lay concealed in the mountain's depths, the bold young man walked on until he came at last to a huge door. He slipped the key into the lock, but before he could even turn it, the door opened by itself.

Then he saw that he was on the other side of the mountain, in a sunny cave whose mouth was somewhat like a balcony. This must be the place the giant had told him of. He walked gingerly to the edge and

found himself looking down over a yawning precipice. There was no way he could go on from here, and suddenly he heard the great door slam behind him with a clang. But the brave lad did not panic. He remembered he must burn the giant's hair, and when he did so a miracle took place! There before him stood a horse with wings.

"Tell me what you want of me," it asked him in a human voice.

"I want you to take me to find the sad nightingale," replied the boy, without a trace of fear.

"Then climb up on my back, hold tightly to my mane, and off we go," the winged horse told him.

A moment later, the fearless lad was soaring through the boundless sky, clinging tightly to the horse and gazing down in wonder at the mountains and the plains, the lakes and forests below.

At length they reached a mountain even taller than the last one, a towering mass which reared up to the heavens and stretched from one side of the horizon to the other.

The horse began to fly in circles in front of this awesome cliff and the boy grew uneasy. He did not see how they could possibly get over it.

"Don't worry," the winged horse reassured him. "This mountain splits in two, then closes up again. As soon as it opens, I'll fly you through."

The horse had hardly spoken when there was a fearsome, grinding roar, the whole earth trembled and the great rock wall before them slowly parted. The horse winged through the opening like a bolt of lightning. They had barely reached the other side when there was an explosion louder than a thousand thunderclaps together, and the towering walls closed back upon each other with a shaking even more terrible than before.

The marvellous horse kept flying, straight and true, until they reached a palace which had forty

towers. There it glided down to earth and the boy climbed off its back. "The sad nightingale is here," it told him. "Search and you will find it. I shall wait for you, but you must hurry, for this place is the home of the forty dragons." Quite unafraid, the lad went off alone and soon came to a garden. He could hear birdsong all around him – but which one was the sad nightingale? He moved on silently, until his ears made out a song as sad as weeping. He went further still into the garden until, beneath a flowering lemon tree, he saw a maiden sleeping on a marble seat. Upon her knees was spread a beautiful white scarf, embroidered all around with scarlet roses, and on that scarf there perched a nightingale whose song was like the fall of bitter tears.

The boy's heart hammered in his breast. He knew that this must be the nightingale he sought. Slowly he crept closer, and when the bird saw him it nestled in the folds of the cloth and made no attempt to fly

away. The lad quickly lifted the scarf by its four corners, with the nightingale safely tucked inside, and ran off as fast as his legs could carry him.

But the sudden movement woke the sleeping girl, who started up and shrieked, "Thief! Thief! A thief has stolen my nightingale! Run, brothers!"

In a flash, the forty dragons slithered out of the forty towers and began to hunt him down. Behind them ran their sister, who was really a dragon herself.

Quick as a flash, the brave lad vaulted on the horse's back as it spread its broad wings and soared into the sky.

The dragons sped desperately after them, hurling rocks, but they were already far too high for the stones to find their target. Even so, the dragons kept up the chase, hoping they would trap the fugitives against the towering rock wall which barred the way.

The moment the winged horse reached the mountain, though, it opened up to let them through, then closed again immediately, leaving the dragons on the other side. There was nothing more that they could do, and they went back to the palace gnashing their teeth in rage.

The marvellous flying horse sped swiftly through the clouds, and soon arrived back at the mouth of the cave which overlooked the precipice. The boy climbed down from the horse's back and gratefully stroked its glossy neck. Then he went over to the great iron door, opened it with the giant's key and made his way back through the tunnel to the other side of the mountain.

"I've done it, giant! Look, here's the nightingale!" he cried, giving the giant back his golden key.

The giant was delighted that the boy had found the nightingale. After all, the brave lad had given him his sight back, and that was no small thing!

"You see how fortune smiles upon the bold?" he

said. "Off you go now, lad, and good luck on your journey home."

"Thank you for all you've done," the boy replied, "I'll never forget the debt I owe you for helping me so much." His heart bursting with joy, he bid the giant farewell and went off down the mountain, carefully holding the headscarf with the nightingale inside.

He still had a long and difficult way ahead of him, but he rested wherever he found shade, ate well from his never-failing store of bread and cheese, and always shared it with the nightingale in case the bird should die of hunger. And so, by easy stages, he made his way back over all the mountains until at last he reached a place where two roads met beside a well. It was a hot day and he decided to sit down for a while and rest, enjoy a drink of water and take a bite to eat. Just at that moment, what should he see a little further off but a sorry-looking fellow sprawled exhausted in the dust. The boy went up to him, and when he did, he got the shock of his life: it was Snooty! Yes, it was his master's once-proud son, but how he had come down in the world! He was dirty, ragged, and there was no sign of his horse. Yet by him still stood the empty cage he had set off with all those months before, bursting with haughty hopes. But now he sat there miserably hunched up, his proud dreams faded.

The boy greeted him kindly, took out some bread and cheese from the sack and sat down to share a meal.

"Don't look so miserable," he told him, "for in this scarf is the sad nightingale, and if I marry the princess I'll invite you to come and live in the palace with us."

Yet the merchant's son was not only proud but wicked and cunning, too. Already he was hatching a devilish scheme.

"If he imagines I'm going to the palace to be the servant of a mere apprentice, then he can think again," he told himself. And then, out loud, he said, "Now we've eaten our fill, we could do with a drink of water, but I see no bucket at the well, only a rope."

"What can we do, then?" asked the boy.

"Here's what: You lower me on the rope so I can drink, then I'll let you down so you can have your turn, and after that we'll leave."

The apprentice lowered Snooty into the well. When he came up again, he said, "Before I let you down, let's put the bird in my cage, in case it escapes."

The boy agreed, and so they put the nightingale into the cage. But he carefully folded the headscarf and put it in his pocket. Then Snooty lowered him down the well. And, of course, the moment he had done so, he grabbed the cage with the nightingale in it and took to his heels.

He ran straight to the king.

The palace filled with cries of joy when it was learned that a brave young man had brought back the sad nightingale. They immediately dressed Snooty in fine clothes, while the princess, who felt her strength returning with the happy news, rose from her sickbed and ran to see. She tried to give it food from her own hands, but the nightingale was as sad as ever and would neither eat nor drink nor sing. The unhappy maiden fell back on her bed and now her sickness was much worse than before.

However, the young apprentice was not trapped down the well for long. The very next day a shepherd heard his shouts and hauled him up again.

Of course, the shepherd wanted to know how the lad had got himself in such a scrape, but there was no time to be lost and so he only said, "I slipped and fell" before thanking his rescuer and running off towards the palace.

The guards at the gateway did not want to let him in, but the boy kept crying that the sad nightingale had been stolen from him, and when the princess heard this, she ordered the guards to open the gates and lead him to her chamber.

Her father and mother were there, and in a corner stood Snooty, too. When the lad's eyes met his, he froze with fear.

"Most reverend majesty, and worthy queen," the boy announced as he came into the chamber, "it was I who found the sad nightingale, and anything else this fellow may have told you is a pack of shameless lies." And with this he told them how he had tracked down the bird and brought it back, and how the other youth had stolen it and left him down the well to rot.

As the apprentice's tale unfolded, Snooty began to tremble like a leaf and grew as pale as death. He tried to bluff it out, claiming it was the lad who was

the liar and not he, but the words came stumbling out of his mouth and made no sense, and everybody could see who was really telling the truth.

"Yes, but what about the nightingale?" the king broke in. "It will neither eat nor sing, and now the princess is even sicker than before."

Then the apprentice took from his pocket the white silk headscarf embroidered all around with scarlet roses, and laid it on the knees of the princess.

A cry of joy escaped the poor girl's pale, drawn lips when she saw her lost scarf lying there, and she immediately sat up in her bed.

Now the lad took the cage, opened its little door, and the nightingale hopped out and perched upon the headscarf which lay across the knees of the princess. And straight away it burst into a song of purest joy, happy again at last.

Tears rolling down her cheeks, the lovely girl

91

stretched out her palm and the little bird hopped into it. Gently closing her fingers round its body, she brought the tiny creature to her lips and kissed it.

And then a miracle took place.

Before the astonished eyes of all those in the chamber stood the princess's lost brother. No longer did the beautiful maiden hold the nightingale in her hand, but instead she grasped the fingers of the little boy she loved so deeply.

Brother and sister, father and mother fell into each other's arms, weeping with joy now that happy days had come back to the royal house.

The brave apprentice was almost as delighted as they were, for he now realised that in bringing back the sad nightingale he had reunited the princess with her lost brother. Who knows what evil witch had transformed the little prince into a nightingale and given the bird to the sister of the forty dragons, beyond the tall mountains, in a place that nobody

could ever reach? And by now you will have realised yourselves that the only way to turn the nightingale into a boy again was by his sister's kiss, which
seemed utterly impossible when the nightingale had
been spirited away to a remote spot there seemed no
hope of getting to.

And yet the impossible had been achieved, as so
many things can be, when a noble cause lends wings
to our determination. Now that the fearless apprentice had brought happiness and gaiety where grief
and suffering had reigned, the merrymaking spread
throughout the palace, and it lasted nine whole days.

Three days they feasted the return of the lost
prince. Three days they feasted in honour of the
splendid lad who had brought back the sad nightingale. And three days and nights they celebrated his
marriage to the loveliest maiden in the world.

As for Snooty, the king was all for punishing him,
and harshly, too, but the kind apprentice, who had

now become a prince, begged the king to spare him. They let him go unharmed and from that day on, or so folks say, his foolish pride quite vanished.

As for the new-crowned prince, he could never forget the debt he owed to the giant who had helped him, and so it was that once a year he would make the journey to his cave, always carrying his mother's scissors, and trim the giant's eyebrows.

And that is the end of the story, children, and time you were asleep.

The Dress that Went into a Walnut

here was once a king who had ten sons, and how proud it made him feel!

"I have ten sons!" he would boast at every opportunity, as if he were saying he was the mightiest ruler in the world.

But it was not only his ten sons he took such pride in. He also liked to boast about an apple tree which stood in his garden, a lovely tree with spreading branches which produced great red apples so delicious that there were no others like them in the whole wide world.

If ever a guest arrived on a visit from some other kingdom, there were two things he never failed to do: present his ten sons to the visitor and offer him a gift of his marvellous apples.

But there came a year when every time he sent his servants to pick apples, they would find not a single ripe fruit on the branches. The king was beside himself with worry, and in the end he decided to consult his royal counsellors.

"My lord the king," pronounced the eldest of them, "the answer seems quite clear. Someone has been coming in the night and picking all the ripest and the reddest of your apples. You must set guards to keep a watch on them and catch the thief."

Set guards? Why guards, when the king had ten brave sons? How brave, we shall soon see.

And so he ordered two of them to go that night and watch in secret, to find out how the red apples were so mysteriously disappearing.

The two young princes buckled on their golden swords, took up their tall spears and proudly went to keep a night watch on the garden.

They were standing in the shadows when suddenly they heard an evil hissing, and a moment later they spied a hideous monster lumbering towards them. The moment they set eyes on it, the princes were overcome with fear. It never crossed their minds to draw their swords; they just took to their heels like rabbits.

"Father!" they gasped, the moment they got back, "There's a terrible creature, a huge monster that comes at night and eats your apples up!"

"Then tomorrow four of you will go and kill it," ordered the king. Yet even though there were four of them next night, the moment the princes saw the monster they were frightened out of their wits and ran back to their father white with terror.

The king was far from pleased, but the monster

had to be dealt with and so he decided to send all ten next time.

The following evening the princes all set off, but on the way they sat down to talk the matter over, and decided not to go in search of the hideous creature after all. Instead, they went to a tavern where they ate, drank and danced the night away. In the morning they returned to their father and told him that the monster stealing apples from the garden was so huge and horrible that a whole army would not be able to defeat it.

The king was sitting on his throne, fuming with rage, when who should appear but Carrot-top. This was the scornful name the king's sons called a young lad with red hair who worked in the palace kitchens.

"Ha! Ha! Ha!" roared the king when he heard that Carrot-top had come to announce that he intended to slay the monster, a creature not even his ten bold sons together could destroy.

He gave him a bow and arrows and told him he could try, yet far from admiring the brave fellow's daring and wishing he could kill the monster, he hoped that he would not come back alive. What really maddened him was the thought that if the kitchen-boy did slay the beast, it would be a mortal insult to his ten fine sons. All the same, he ordered the princes to follow secretly and see what happened.

Now when night fell, the boy went to the garden, lay in wait and the instant he saw the monster coming shot off an arrow at it. He hit the monster in the back. It let out a howl of pain, but before he could take aim again it dragged itself away and disappeared into the dark.

When daylight came, the brave lad spotted the monster's footprints and decided he would go in search of it. But he had not gone far before he ran into the king's ten sons instead.

"I wounded the beast," he told them, "and now I'm off to track it down and finish it." And with these words he began to follow the pawprints in the earth and the drops of blood which had trickled from the monster's wounded body. The ten princes followed close behind, but not too close!

The trail ended by a well, and the bold young fellow knew the beast must have its lair there.

"Lower me down," he told the king's sons, without a moment's hesitation. The ten princes cast sidelong glances at each other as if to say, 'Let the monster devour him and have done with it', and they quickly tied a rope round Carrot-top's waist and lowered him into the well.

At the bottom there was no water at all, but a cave instead and in its depths lay the monster, huddled in a ball. Quick as a flash, Carrot-top loosed another arrow which hit the creature squarely in the head and left it lifeless.

"You've saved me!" came a voice behind him, and turning in surprise he saw a maiden as fresh and lovely as a mountain spring.

"How did you get down here?" he asked her in a wondering voice.

"Do not remind me of it," the maid replied. "I am an orphan and have no-one in the world. I fell into the hands of evil men, who beat me cruelly and dragged me off to be sold as a slave in the bazaars of Anatolia. On the way I managed to escape and clambered down this well to stop them finding me. But I could not climb out again, and the next day at dawn that monster came. It had a human voice and promised it would not devour me, but neither would it let me go, for it had always longed for the company of a fair maiden. I have been here for seven whole days and nights, but now at last I have been saved."

"Up you go, then," said the young man and tugging on the rope he shouted, "I've killed the monster, and I've found a maiden down here in the well. Pull her out first and then let down the rope for me."

"But are you sure they'll pull you out as well?" the maiden whispered.

"And why should they leave me here?"

"I cannot say – but something tells me that is what will happen."

"I shouldn't think so. After all, they are the king's ten sons. What should they have to fear from me?"

"If they are good men, nothing. But you have killed a fearsome monster, and if they are wicked they may well be afraid of you. Since I owe you my life, I must tell you how to save yourself if they do indeed abandon you down here. Very soon, two rams will come, one as white as snow and the other black like coal. Jump straight onto the white ram's back and it will bring you out. But if you mount the

black ram, it will take you even deeper underground, and it will be difficult or maybe even impossible to make your way back up again. When you do get out of here, however, you must come to find me. You may need to set me free a second time, for I fear the king will make a slave of me. But I shall wait for you, however long you take."

"I cannot believe that any harm will come to either of us, but whatever happens I shall find you and secure your happiness," the brave lad answered, his heart swelling with joy to think the lovely maid would wait for him, however long he was away. "But do not be afraid," he added, "we will both be rescued now."

"I hope so, but I don't believe it," said the girl, "so take this walnut. It was given to me by a water-nymph, and impossible as it may seem, there is a wedding dress inside. It has a thousand pleats and is embroidered with the sun, the moon and all the stars of the heavens. If you do not return, the dress will never be of any use to me, but if you deliver it into my hands then I shall wear it as a bride and be your wife."

"Even if I descend into the underworld and am offered a princess as a bride, I shall return in search of you and make you mine," the young man answered. With these words he tied the rope around the maiden's waist and the king's sons drew her up.

And then exactly what the girl had feared took place. The ten princes, dazzled by her beauty, left Carrot-top down there in the well and dragged the unfortunate maiden off with them.

"What are you doing?" she cried out in despair. "How can you leave that brave lad down the well when he has killed the monster?"

"Listen, girl," they answered threateningly, "we are the ones who killed the monster. That's the tale the king will hear — and just make sure you don't deny it, or that will be the end of you. Like it or not, you'll do exactly what we tell you, but it will all turn out for your own good, since you'll be married off to one of us and become a royal princess."

"But the young man! You must pull him out!" the maiden cried. But all in vain. The princes wouldn't hear of it and dragged her cruelly away.

When they got back to their father's palace, they told him boastfully how they had killed the monster and released this lovely girl it had been holding prisoner in the well.

"And as for Carrot-top," they added, "the hideous creature gobbled him alive. But now, father, we beg you to decide which of us will marry this beautiful young maiden."

"My sons," the king replied, "words cannot describe the joy you bring me. You are indeed ten fearless princes, and worthy of great honours. And do not waste your tears on Carrot-top – the lad was

looking for trouble and he found it. As for this maiden here, whose loveliness outshines the sun, she is worthy to be made a queen, so I shall take her as my bride."

The king's sons exchanged sullen glances at these words, while the girl's heart sank into her shoes. But she was not about to admit defeat.

"Your majesty," she said, "I shall wait for the young man whom I love, and if he is fated never to return, then I shall never marry."

The king was stung by her reply. "Seven times I have been wed," he told himself, "and no woman ever turned me down before. Does a mere slip of a girl now think she can refuse me? But let her speak her piece, for I shall make her mine, regardless of her wishes."

At that very moment, down in the well, Carrot-top saw two rams emerge from a cleft in the rock. One was white and the other black. He took a leap at the white ram's back, but it swerved aside. While he was still in mid-air, the black ram slid between his open legs, and in an instant he found himself sitting on its back and being carried deeper and ever deeper down into the bowels of the earth. After a long, wild run it brought him to the kingdom of the underworld. There, outside a city, the ram set down the lad and disappeared.

The underworld was strange, but beautiful. The sky was the colour of rose petals, the clouds sea-blue, the sun was a sparkling diamond and the trees resembled giant flowers of every hue. The city that spread out before him was like something from a fairy tale. He made his way towards the nearest house, a neat, well cared-for little cottage and the door was opened by a kindly old woman. The young man asked her for a drink of water.

"Alas, we have no water in our city," she replied. "A monster nobody can kill has dried the springs up with its magic tail, and our chief soothsayer tells us the water will only run again if the monster devours the daughter of our king."

"So what have you done about it?" asked the lad.

"What else could we do, my son? We didn't want to die of thirst, so in the end we steeled our hearts and this very morning we tied the poor girl to a tree which stands by the great spring on that mountain over there. Now our only hope is that the monster will somehow take pity on our innocent princess."

The moment brave Carrot-top heard these words, he ran off up the mountain to the spot where the princess had been left, and hid himself behind a bush. Night fell and the monster came. The lad had kept his bow strung all this time, and now he loosed an arrow. It struck the monster in the belly, but could not pierce its scaly hide. He aimed again and hit it in the head, but once again the arrow bounced off, as if it had struck a rock.

"Let's try to hit him in that magic tail of his," the boy then said, and drawing his bow a third time, he planted an arrow in the tip of the creature's thrashing tail.

That did the trick! The hideous beast sank lifeless to the ground, and as it did the springs began to flow again. Carrot-top ran over to the princess and untied the ropes that bound her. He helped her down the mountain, as far as the first houses in the city, then said, "Now I must leave."

"No, come with me to the palace," the princess begged. "My father will want to meet you, and give you the reward which you deserve."

"But I don't belong here," said the lad. "I must make my way back to the upper world."

"Why go to the upper world? Your king up there is evil. We have no evil men down here and everything is more beautiful. Now you have killed the monster there is nothing in our world to give us

113

pain or sadness."

"It may be as you say, but my country is up there, and that is where I wish to go."

And with these words he left the princess to make her own way back to the palace.

Next day, the King's heralds came crying through the streets:

"Whoever killed the monster must present himself immediately at the palace, for our royal master desires to give him his daughter's hand in marriage."

But the brave young man was in love with the fair maiden of the well, and when he heard the king was asking for him he went back to the old woman's cottage and begged her to hide him.

When three days passed and no one had appeared, the king sent his heralds out a second time, but again without result.

So then he sent them out for a third time, to shout these words:

"Our mighty lord the king wishes to celebrate the rescue of our city and his daughter and so he invites you, one and all, young and old, to feast at his expense in the great square by the palace."

But when the people came and the food was served, soldiers were out in force among the crowd and made very sure that no one tried to take home anything to eat. This is how they caught the old woman, just as she was slipping a slice of pie into her bag. They ran to report the matter to the king.

"Go to her house immediately," he ordered. "Arrest the man you find there and bring him straight to me."

The soldiers rushed to the old woman's cottage. There they found the red-haired boy and marched him off to the palace.

When the king set eyes upon the fine young man they brought into his presence, he knew at once that this must be the hero who had killed the monster. Just to make sure, he called his daughter in and she recognised her rescuer at once.

Then the king said, "I promised I would give my daughter to whoever killed the monster – but to you I give my throne as well."

"Most reverend majesty," replied the young man with regret, "I am carrying the wedding dress of the maiden who awaits me. She is the girl I wish to take for my wife, and I desire neither a throne nor kingly powers. But if you wish to offer me some other reward, then all I ask is that you tell me how to reach the upper world."

Now the king was a kind man, like all the people of the underworld, and he admired the bold young fellow for giving such an answer. Yet at the same time he was sorry he could not persuade him to take his daughter's hand in marriage, for the lad was not only bold and fearless but seemed to have a noble soul. But as for how the king could help him, that he did not know.

"It is a hard task you have set me," he replied, "but perhaps my seven wise men can be of some assistance. Let me take you to them."

And so the king led Carrot-top through the palace until they reached the chamber of the seven wise men. Seeing that all of them were present, the king announced:

"I wish to ask a favour of you, gentlemen. Can any of you tell this young man how to reach the upper world? It is he who saved us from the monster's curse, and now we must pay him back by helping him return to the place where he belongs, for he feels himself a stranger here."

"If only I could be of help," the first wise man replied, "but, alas, I must confess I do not know."

"Neither do I, to tell the truth," added the second.

"Nor I," "Nor I," responded each in turn.

"We must consult the seven great books," the first one finally decided.

"Go through them word by word," the king commanded. "Leave not a page unturned, for some way must be found." And he left them to find an answer in the seven great books, while the young man stood waiting anxiously.

"I've found it!" one of the wise men suddenly exclaimed. "Look, it says it here: 'The upper world can only be reached with the help of the fresh-killed snake'."

"In other words?" enquired the lad.

"There are no other words. That's it."

"And is that all you're going to tell me?"

"But that is all the great book says," replied the wise man; and Carrot-top left the chamber looking very disappointed.

He walked and walked, not knowing where his steps were leading him, till in the end he was overcome with weariness and lay down beneath a tree. High up in its branches he could see a nest of baby eagles.

"Kaa! Kaaa!" he suddenly heard the young ones cry in fear – and not without reason, for a snake was slithering up the tree and making rapidly towards their nest. It did not have time to do the eaglets any harm, though, for the brave lad brought it tumbling down with an arrow through its lifeless head.

Moments later, he heard a rush of wings and saw two great birds hovering over him. They were the parents of the eaglets in the nest above.

"Aah!" they croaked angrily, "so you're the one who keeps on coming here and eating up our chicks so we can't have any children!" And they swooped down, talons bared to claw his eyes out.

"No! No!" cried the chicks. "This brave man just saved us from the snake!"

The two eagles looked down and saw the fresh-killed snake. Then they opened wide their spreading wings to make a shade for the young man to sleep

beneath, for they could see that he was very tired.

When he awoke, they asked if they could be of any service.

"Yes," replied Carrot-top "If it is in your power, I would like you to carry me to the upper world."

"That is no easy thing to ask," replied the eagles, "but when we see that serpent lying dead, we feel we owe the favour to you. Climb on the back of one of us and we shall carry you. But when you hear a "Kra!" you must jump across to the other eagle's back. Like that, we'll get some rest during the flight and will find the strength to take you where you want."

The young man mounted one of the eagles and they soared into the heavens.

They had been flying for some time when he heard a "Kra!" from the eagle he was seated on, and he jumped across to the other eagle's back. A similar length of time had passed when he heard another

"Kra!", and he hopped across again. Twelve times he changed his seat before they reached the upper world, and when at last they landed, the eagles left the red-haired lad within walking distance of a city. When the two great birds had disappeared from view, he took the road that led into the town. Having arrived, he did not know where to go, but at last he walked into a tailor's shop and said:

"Will you take me on as your apprentice, master? All I ask is a little food to eat."

The tailor let him in and made him his assistant. The lad worked hard and well, but the beautiful maiden of the well was never far from his thoughts.

She, meanwhile, was still a prisoner in the palace, and every day the king kept pestering her to marry him.

"You will become a queen and live cradled in wealth and honours. What else could you possibly desire?" he reminded her time and time again. But the lovely maiden thought always of the young man she adored, and searched to find a way of escaping from the king, whose attentions became daily more unwelcome.

"Listen, my lovely one," he said to her one day, "ask whatever you wish of me, and even if you set the most impossible task in the whole wide world I'll do it for your sake, just as long as you promise to become my wife."

When the girl heard these words, her face lit up with hope and she replied:

"Yes, there is one thing I long for, but I don't know if my wish can ever be fulfilled. I want to be married in a wedding dress with a thousand pleats, embroidered with the sun, the moon and all the stars in the wide heavens, and yet so delicately woven that it can fit inside a walnut shell. And one more thing: I wish the man who brings this gift to become my loving husband."

"At last!" the old king cried. "Now I shall make you mine, for I, and I alone, can carry out your wish."

"But if by any chance you can't? And if another comes who can, will you give me your solemn word that you will let me marry whoever presents me with the wedding dress?"

"I give you my word," replied the king, certain that no one else could make her such a gift.

Having said this, the king sent out a proclamation announcing he would cut the head off every tailor in the kingdom unless, within three days, one could be found to sew for him a wedding dress which had a thousand pleats, embroidered with the sun, the moon and all the stars that shine down from the heavens – and all this to fit inside a walnut shell.

Next morning, a great cry of despair went up from every tailor's shop throughout the land. The tailor who had taken on young Carrot-top as his apprentice sat weeping hopeless tears. His wife wept, too, and their children wept along with them.

The first of the three dreaded days ticked by, and the second was drawing all too soon towards its close, when the young man told them,

"Weep no more. Just bring me walnuts and a little brandy and in the morning we will pay a visit on the king and deliver him the wedding dress. Then neither you nor any tailor in the kingdom will come to any harm."

They ran to fetch the walnuts and a flask of brandy, adding some almonds and a pot of honey for good measure.

Yet the tailor could not set his mind at rest, and when evening came he watched in secret to see if his apprentice was working on the dress. To his dismay, he saw instead the young man breaking open almond shells and walnuts, munching away and swigging from the brandy flask. Shaking his head in despair, the tailor crept back up to bed. The next morning, his last on earth he feared, he went down to the shop to find his assistant fast asleep.

"All is lost!" groaned the tailor, and the whole family burst into tears once more.

Their wailing woke the young man up. He washed, straightened his clothes and calmly told the tailor,

"Come on, it's time to take the wedding dress to the king."

"What dress? Have you gone mad? Where is it, then?"

"Why, where else would it be? Inside this walnut shell, of course."

He took the maiden's walnut from his pocket, opened it and drew out the dress. It shimmered in his hands, lovely beyond all belief. The tailor was beside himself with joy, and the whole family flew into each other's arms, sobbing with relief.

Carrot-top folded the dress back in the walnut shell and put it in his pocket once again.

128

"But I am the one who should present it to the king," the tailor protested.

Now the tailor was not an evil man, of course, but the young fellow was learning from experience, and he thought,

"I didn't take the king's ten sons for bad men, either, but look how they left me down the well." And so he took another walnut from his pocket and gave that to the tailor, saying,

"Here you are, then. But we shall go to the king together," he added.

When the appointed hour arrived, the king was waiting anxiously in the palace. Beside him stood the lovely maiden, who could not wait to see whether the brave young man would come with the walnut shell that held her wedding dress.

Sure enough, a moment later the heralds sounded their trumpets, the great doors opened wide and into the palace stepped a tailor and her rescuer with

130

his shock of fiery red hair.

The maiden's face lit up with joy, while the king turned deathly pale.

"How did you get here, young Carrot-top?" he gasped. "I thought you had been eaten by the monster."

"Your majesty, it was I who killed the monster, not the princes."

"How dare you say such things to me! Do you realise what you could be made to pay for insulting my brave sons?"

"No, king, you are the one who should be made to pay, and richly too," the maiden interrupted. "For the truth is, it was this young hero who slew the beast and saved me when I was imprisoned in its lair."

Then she told the king all that had really happened, and how the ten princes had forced her to keep silence.

131

When the king heard, he turned upon his sons in fury.

"Get out of here!" he screamed. "Let me never set eyes on you again!" And he ordered his soldiers to drive them from the palace there and then.

Next, turning to the tailor and the brave young man, he asked,

"And what brings you here? You haven't brought the dress, by any chance?"

"Oh yes indeed, most reverend sire," replied the tailor, handing him the walnut with a deep bow.

"Thanks be to God!" the king sighed in relief, happily fondling the walnut which the tailor had presented him.

"My lord," the young man then asked boldly," I hope you will allow me to offer this fair maid a walnut, too?" And without waiting for an answer he quickly gave the lovely girl the walnut which was in his pocket.

The king broke open the nut he had been given by the tailor but there was nothing but a kernel in it, and a rotten one at that.

The girl then opened hers, drew out the wedding dress and threw herself into the young man's arms.

"What's going on here?" spluttered the king, ready to burst, he was so furious.

"You promised me," the maiden answered calmly, "that I could wed the man who brought the wedding dress I asked for. Here is the dress. And here is the man who gave it to me, so give us your blessing now." And with these words she took her hero's hand and led him before the king.

Now whether he was too proud to go back on his promise or, more likely, because he had no other choice, the king agreed "You have my blessing," but he muttered it so low they hardly heard the words. Then his voice rose from a murmur to a scream:

"And as for you, you so-called tailor, I'll tear you

limb from limb!"

"Not when we have chosen him as our best man," replied the young man firmly.

What could the king say now? He stood there a long moment, completely lost for words. He thought and thought, then finally made up his mind.

"I have grown so used to always getting my way, and here I am, defeated in my turn. Well done, the pair of you! And I say this from the bottom of my heart, for it was your virtue and your love which got the better of me, two words I never knew the power of till today. I wish you both long life and happiness, and I say it now in all sincerity."

He stood there for a moment and then added,

"Rule with wisdom and with kindness, for I give you my throne as well. I have grown old. I have been slow to realise it, but at least I have done so when the time is right. And now, all speed! For tomorrow there shall be a royal wedding!"

134

A wedding there was, and they feasted and danced for nine joyful days and nights.

I was at the wedding, too,
Dancing and feasting nine nights through.

The Marble Princess

nce upon a time there lived a couple who had only one child. But what a child: a bold and spirited boy worth ten ordinary children.

All they had besides were two cows and a small field to graze them in. Yet what was the good of two poor cows, especially when their ribs showed through their hides? How much milk could they give? So how could their owners lead anything but a miserable existence?

Still, they could have lived rather better if they had let their cows onto the big meadow next door, which always produced plenty of grass and where no animal had ever grazed.

"Father," said the boy one day, "why don't we let our cows feed in the meadow next to ours?"

"Because, my child, that meadow belongs to the wicked giant, and all he ever thinks about is doing evil deeds."

The boy, however, could not see why so much grass should go to waste, and why a poor couple's cows should not graze there. "It's not fair!" he would mutter. And just as his parents were good, kind-hearted people so, too, was the boy. And he was bold as well, so if it ever came to challenging the giant he would not hesitate a moment.

"Listen, father," he said one day, "I think we should let our cows go into the giant's meadow."

"Are you mad, my son? All he wants is an excuse to knock our cottage down and take our meadow, just as he has done with all his other neighbours."

"But, father, if that's the sort of creature that he is, then we ought to fight him."

"Oh dear," muttered the poor man to himself, "my son is going crazy!"

And to make sure they didn't run into any trouble he began to lead the cows to pasture on his own, always taking great care that they didn't get into the giant's meadow. The boy, who by now had reached fifteen, had one ambition in life: to put up such a fight against the wicked giant that he would no longer be able to do people any harm. But, as things were, his father wouldn't give him a single chance to pasture the cows himself. One day, however, his father fell ill and had to stay at home to be cared for by his wife. Then, as there was no other solution, he told his son to go and pasture their two animals.

"But be very careful not to let them get into the giant's meadow, for if they do, we're lost."

"All right, father," replied the boy. He didn't want to upset the sick old man, and so he didn't allow the cows to stray.

140

The boy kept his word through all the days that followed, so when he got his health back, the father allowed him to go on taking out the cows.

But one evening, when the boy came home, the beasts had stomachs as enormous as balloons from eating so much grass.

'How did they manage to find so much to eat?' the father wondered. Suddenly his blood ran cold. "My boy, you didn't let them get into the wicked giant's meadow by any chance?"

"Yes," replied the boy. "I let them in, and I intend to let them graze there every day."

When he heard this, his father froze. "Are we going to quarrel with a giant like that? Are we seeking our own ruin?"

"I won't let him do us any harm, father. Our troubles are over now. His are just beginning."

'Now our son has gone completely mad,' said the poor man to himself. 'But then, what sort of life is this we lead? What does it matter if fate overtakes us an hour earlier than was intended?'

So the boy set off again next day to pasture the cows in the forbidden meadow, and this time with his father's blessing; but when he arrived the giant himself was standing there.

"What are you doing here, you miserable little worm?" he bellowed fiercely.

"I'm letting the cows eat here because there's lots of grass."

"And do you know who this meadow belongs to?"

"Yes, I do. But I brought them to feed here because otherwise the grass would go to waste."

"How dare you speak to me like that! Don't you realise who I am?"

"Yes, you're the wicked giant who wouldn't give a glass of water to his own guardian angel. But I'm not afraid of you!"

"Did you say you're not afraid of me?"

142

"Yes. I'm not afraid of you."

"What impudence! Very well, then, since you're not afraid, come along with me. I'll show you where I live, and then we'll see if you're afraid or not!"

"All right. Let's go!"

They walked for some time through the giant's meadows and his ploughlands until eventually they found themselves in front of a huge, lofty castle.

"This is where I live!" said the giant, bursting with pride, as the guards swung the heavy iron gates open.

They entered a wide courtyard, one half fenced off by metal bars, behind which paced a crowd of animals, from cats and dogs to wolves and lions.

"What are all those animals?" the young cowherd asked.

"Don't ask. You'll find out soon enough when you join them."

They carried on and entered the castle.

"Would you like to see all the rooms? Have a good look, and you'll realise just how much I'm worth. But it won't do you any good, for in the end you'll finish up just like all the rest."

"I'm not going to finish up like anybody. But yes, I would like to see all the rooms."

"Excellent. Take these keys and unlock them." He handed him forty keys. "Explore at your leisure!" he invited in a mocking voice, and left him alone.

The boy opened the first door.

All he could see inside the room was a single pair of slippers. He put them on, and at once became so light that he could jump up and touch the ceiling without the slightest effort. If he had been outdoors, he could have hopped across the broadest river.

He recalled the giant's words: 'It won't do you any good.' "But it's going to do me a lot of good!" exclaimed the bold youth and he popped the slippers into his bag.

He unlocked the second room and found a small sword with its scabbard. The sword was lying on a round table which was actually no more than a huge log. The boy touched the log with the point of the sword, at which it immediately split into two.

"So this is magic, too," said the boy, and, sliding the sword into its sheath, he put it in his bag.

He unlocked the third room and found nothing but a cap. He put it on and immediately became invisible. He took it off and became visible once more. "This will be useful, too," he said with a smile, and popped it into his bag.

He unlocked the next room. It was full of gold florins. He opened the next. It was heaped with diamonds. He opened another. It was piled with pearls. All the other rooms in turn were filled with similar riches. The boy was dazzled by the giant's treasures, but he didn't keep anything. 'What I've already taken will be plenty for me,' he said to himself.

146

Two rooms remained. He unlocked the first, and what did he see? On a bed carved with matchless craftsmanship there lay a girl as beautiful as any angel. At first the cowherd thought she was asleep, but he soon realised she had been turned into marble. His heart beat faster with admiration for her beauty, yet with pain as well, because he pitied her. But it also beat with anger against the wicked giant for doing this evil thing to her.

"I must release her – but how?" he cried. "Perhaps I will find a way when I see what secret is hidden in the final room – for if the giant has set a trap for me, that is where it will be. If I come out of this victorious, what happiness will follow! Everything will end joyfully. I shall release this beautiful maiden and, if she will have me, I will make her my wife!"

Very cautiously, the boy opened the last door. And there before him, with a welcoming smile, stood a tall, striking woman with slanting eyebrows over

148

large dark eyes, and a chin jutting with pride and power. But at the back of the room, which was as vast as a great hall, on a lofty, throne-like seat, there sat the evil giant himself.

The woman, who was neither very young nor very old, was holding a rod in her hand. With a wordless gesture, she invited the young man to come forward. He knew at once that he was dealing with a witch, and only took a couple of short steps. She in turn took two and, with a honeyed smile, stretched out her wand to touch his head. But with one lightning movement the boy snatched the wand from her grasp and snapped it in two. That did the trick! The witch uttered a cry of terror and despair. But worst of all the wicked giant toppled headlong from his lofty throne, striking his head a fatal blow.

Now the young herdsman possessed such a kind heart that he felt pity even for the terrible giant, and he ran to his assistance while the witch, her proud

149

wings clipped, cowered in a corner of the hall.

"I am past any help," the giant groaned. "I know my time has come. I have been defeated, and you have escaped my clutches. You have not been turned into an animal like the others you saw down in the courtyard, creatures that were once all human beings. Now my castle, with all my riches, my guards and my servants, is yours. You have the forty keys. The last one also unlocks the outer gate. I wanted to do you harm, but now I shall help you instead. In the rear courtyard you will find a winged white horse which cannot only fly but also speak and prophesy. Make friends with it and it will help you more than you can possibly imagine. Use the slippers to jump with, the sword to cut whatever resists an ordinary blade and the cap to make yourself invisible. You have seen the marble maiden. You saw how beautiful she is! She is a princess who I kidnapped because I desired her for my wife but, who knows why, she would not even look at me. I believed that I could gradually win her round; but my longing for that loveliest of maidens aroused the envy of this jealous witch, and she turned her to marble. Pursue her now until she undoes the spell that turned the princess into stone and releases the people she transformed into animals."

As soon as the witch heard the giant's words, she slipped away. The young man immediately ran after her, but she turned into smoke and vanished. Only her voice could be heard: "I shall be in the Red Tower. You will never find me there — but even if you do, it will be the end of you."

The young man at once returned to the giant. He found him surrounded by servants and guards who had rushed to assist their master. But they could do nothing. The wicked giant was dead.

Then they all bowed low to the young man and said:

"We are yours to command, new master!"

But the young herdsman had no time to lose. He hurried to the rear courtyard and found the horse, which neighed fiercely. The boy stroked its neck and spoke to it as though it were human:

"I want to save the marble princess. I want to rescue the people who have been turned into animals. You must help me to find the witch who has done all these wicked deeds and has now fled to the Red Tower. If you know where that is, and if you want to do some good, then take me there."

This time the horse neighed gently and replied:

"I am the only creature who can tell you where the Red Tower is. Climb onto my back and I will take you there, for I can see you are doing this in a good cause. But it is not such a simple matter to capture this witch and make her obey you. So go into the stable and there, on a shelf, you will find a mirror, a penknife and a piece of cloth. These are all magic,

and you will need them." He then explained to him how these things would prove useful.

The young man went and fetched the things the horse had described and then climbed on its back, and the horse, opening out its huge white wings, soared into the sky.

After they had travelled quite a way, they saw a blue cloud up ahead.

"What is that cloud?" enquired the boy.

"That is no cloud. It is the Young Man of the Sea. Let's go to meet him."

"Greetings," said the cowherd when they reached him.

"Welcome to you, young friend. You're a fine strong lad, and so am I. But to be honest with you, we're not in the same league as that young fellow who overcame the wicked giant."

"And if you were to meet him, what would you wish to call him?"

154

"My brother!"

"Well, I am he – so let's become brothers!"

They threw their arms around each other, kissed, and then, pricking their fingers, they marked each other with their blood, became brothers and journeyed on together.

After a while they reached a city. In the middle of this city, in a big square, a large crowd had gathered. The king was there with his twelve courtiers and they were all grouped around the 'enchanted marble', a huge lump of stone which was so enormous that even six men holding hands could not encircle it.

They were all begging God to cut the marble in two, because they believed that this was the only way to banish misfortune from their city. But God had other things on his mind, and the marble was so hard that no one who tried to cut it or break it could even make a scratch on its surface.

The young herdsman approached and read an inscription on the marble which said:

He who cuts me in two with one blow of his sword
Will bestow on the people a mighty reward.

Then the boy drew his magic sword and struck the marble, which instantly split in two and, marvellous to relate, filled the square with gold florins! There were so many that even after the people had helped themselves to all that they could carry off, as much again was still left for the king.

Everybody then joined in praise of the young man, and the king told him:

"You have done such a great favour to my people and to me that you deserve to take my daughter for your wife."

"Thank you, your majesty, but let your daughter take my brother, the fine Young Man of the Sea, for I am promised to another, and he is as deserving as I am."

The king agreed, and the Young Man of the Sea married the fair princess.

Before they went their separate ways, the young herdsman took out the magic mirror he had found in the stable and gave it to his new brother, saying:

"Take this mirror. If you see it cloud over, that will mean I have great need of you, and you must hurry to my aid."

With these words he mounted the marvellous horse and they soared off into the sky to fly to the Red Tower.

After a while they saw a black cloud.

"Once again, what is that strange cloud?" asked the boy.

"That is no cloud," the horse replied. "It is the Young Man of the Land. Let's go to meet him."

"Greetings," the cowherd said as soon as they drew near.

"Welcome to you, young friend. I'm a fine strong

lad, and so are you. But we're not in the same league as that young fellow who overcame the wicked giant and split the enchanted marble in two with one blow of his sword," said the Young Man of the Land.

"And if the two of you chanced to meet, what would you choose to call him?"

"My brother!"

"Well, I am he – so let's become brothers!"

They threw their arms around each other, they kissed, they pricked their fingers and marked each other with their blood, they became brothers, and continued their journey together.

Soon they reached a large city which was divided in two by a great river.

"That is the 'accursed river'," said the horse. "They call it that because it is bewitched and every so often it bursts its banks and causes untold damage. It will stop wreaking havoc if it changes course, but this will only happen, they say, if someone can cross it in a single bound. And that, as you can see, is quite impossible."

At that moment, they heard from down below town-criers proclaiming that the king would give his daughter to any man who could save the city from the accursed river.

"Let's go down," said the boy, "down there by the palace."

They descended quickly and the young man made his way straight to the king.

"Long life to your majesty!" he said. "I can cross that river with a single bound."

"I don't believe it, but I should like to see you try, for wonders often happen. If you succeed, I shall give you not only my daughter but my throne as well."

The king and his courtiers proceeded to the bank of the river, hoping for some kind of miracle.

Then the boy put on the magic slippers. He gave

160

a great leap and the miracle occurred. The cowherd soared across the broad river. And then another miracle took place: the river began to boil and foam because now, instead of flowing towards the sea, it turned back in its course. As it flowed backwards, it swelled and swelled until it was strong enough to climb the mountain and then roll down the other side. And as it did so, the irresistible surge of its waters cut the mountain in two, creating a deep ravine. Through this ravine now flowed the river, which ceased to be accursed and became blessed, because it now watered a whole plain which had till then lain dry and bare.

Overcome with emotion, the king embraced the young man.

"Now you deserve my daughter and the whole of my kingdom," he said, kissing him.

"No, your majesty," replied the cowherd, whose mind was constantly upon the marble maiden. "But give your daughter to my brother, the Young Man of the Land, who is more deserving than I am. I cannot marry her."

So it happened. And when the two brothers parted, the young man said:

"My brother, take this penknife. Leave it as it is, open. But if you ever see it closed, know that I have need of you and hurry to find me, wherever I may be."

Then he mounted his winged horse and continued his journey toward the Red Tower to find the wicked witch.

Suddenly they saw in front of them a flame-coloured cloud.

"Once again, what is that fiery cloud?"

"That is no cloud. It is the Young Man of the Skies, the son of the Sun."

"Greetings to you," said the cowherd when they reached him.

"Welcome to you, young friend. You're a fine strong lad, and so am I. But we're not in the same league as that young fellow who overcame the wicked giant, who split the enchanted marble with one blow of his sword and who crossed the accursed river in a single bound."

"And if the two of you were to meet, what would you wish to call him?"

"My brother!"

"Well, I am he – so let's become brothers!"

Straightaway they embraced, kissed, pricked fingers and marked each other with their blood and became brothers.

Journeying on towards the Red Tower, they came to a large city. There the king was being driven out of his mind by grief. Every evening, when his daughter went to bed, she would disappear for the whole night, and nobody knew where she went. When she returned, she acted as if she were in a trance. She always managed to elude anyone who was ordered to keep a watch on her to find out what was happening. Now the king had sent out heralds to proclaim that whoever could find out where his daughter went at night might have her as his wife.

The cowherd learnt of this and went to the palace.

"Your majesty, I will discover where your daughter goes."

"Lots of people have told me that, young man. Some of them I trusted. I gave them whatever assistance they needed, but nothing ever came of it. Tell me, though, what help you want from me so that you, too, may make your attempt."

"I need nothing. Only allow me to sleep in her room."

They placed another bed in the princess's chamber, and the young herdsman went there to sleep.

The princess began to tease him:

"Are you the little chap who's going to find out

where I go at night?"

"I am indeed. And I am going to succeed!"

"Then let me tell you that I don't go anywhere. It's just an idea they have got hold of."

"I hope so – because I'm so tired that I don't want to lose my sleep." And he yawned.

The girl lay down on her bed, the young man lay down on his and, after a little while, began to snore so convincingly that you would have sworn he really was asleep.

The princess was taken in by it and got out of bed. Walking on tiptoe, she dressed and left the room.

At once the young man got up, too, donned the magic cap, became invisible and followed her.

They reached a magic glade illuminated by thousands of stars which shed an unearthly brightness. Nereids of dazzling beauty were dancing there, and invisible sprites were singing. As soon as the princess arrived, a water-nymph tripped up to her to swathe her neck in pearls, but in her haste she dropped them. With one bound, the invisible young man ran up and snatched the pearls. The nereids searched for them, but when their efforts came to nothing, they brought her more. Then they all joined the dance together with the princess. At some point, while she was dancing with her arms outstretched, the invisible boy ran up, and before you could say 'knife', he grabbed her ring.

"My ring! I've lost my precious ring!" the princess cried out anxiously.

They searched for it but could find nothing. As for the young herdsman, he ran back to the palace, went to bed and fell asleep, without pretending this time.

At daybreak the princess also returned and when she saw him lying there she laughed mockingly.

When the young man woke up, he went straight to the king.

"I have seen where your daughter goes at night. But I want her to be present when I tell you."

They went and summoned the princess and the young man began his story.

"Yesterday night, when I was lying in my bed and she was lying in hers, I pretended to fall asleep immediately. Indeed, I snored. Then she got up, dressed and left."

"Lies, Father!" shouted the princess.

"I followed her. Don't ask me how it was she didn't notice me. I can prove what I'm saying. We walked a long way, she leading and I following behind, until we reached a magic glade in a forest lighted by hundreds and thousands of stars."

"He's a big liar, Father. Don't listen to him!"

"There," continued the young herdsman, "were dancing lovely water-nymphs with dresses woven from spiders' webs and veils which billowed in the breeze, while the air was filled with the singing of

168

unseen voices. As soon as the princess went to join the dance, a nereid ran to grace her neck with pearls, but she dropped them, and I, unseen by all, picked the pearls up."

"How can you sit there and listen to such a story-teller?" demanded the king's daughter.

"Look, here they are! Or don't you recognise them?" he challenged the princess.

Her face turned scarlet when she saw the pearls.

"No, I don't recognise them," she mumbled, but with confusion written all over her face.

"After I had taken the pearls," the young man continued, "they brought some more and put them on her. Then she joined the dance, but I again, without being seen by anyone, snatched the princess's ring from her hand. Here it is. You must all recognise it."

As soon as the princess saw the ring, she remained rooted to the spot. In despair, she struck her fore-head repeatedly with her hand. And then it was as though she suddenly awakened from a deep slumber, as though she were returning from the world of dreams to reality. For at that moment, certain awful spells were broken which an evil witch had laid on her. She felt as if a burden had been lifted from her and, begging forgiveness from her mother and father, she burst into tears.

"You shouldn't cry, my daughter, but rejoice because you have been cured of a terrible sickness. Here is the young man who has made you well. He must become your husband."

"No, your majesty," replied the young herdsman, "I cannot. My brother, the Young Man of the Skies, will take your daughter. He is more deserving than I am."

And so it came about.

But on parting from his new brother, he gave him the magic cloth and said:

"Take this cloth, brother. If you see it becoming

bloody you must hurry to my side, because I shall have urgent need of you."

And when they had said their farewells, he mounted the winged horse and together they soared into the sky.

"Take me now, my horse, to the tower that you know of. Let's go to seize the witch and force her to lift the spells from the marble princess and from the people she has turned into animals."

Ever obedient, the marvellous horse flew swiftly towards the Red Tower, which could now be faintly seen on the horizon. Eventually they arrived. The young herdsman was dazzled by the sight of it. It was a huge structure whose battlements brushed the clouds. All around it was a lofty wall constructed from enormous stones like those which only a Cyclops could lift. The entrance consisted of two great iron doors bristling with sharp-pointed swords, so that from outside you could not approach.

171

But the young herdsman's marvellous horse had no difficulty entering the tower. He soared over the wall, high above the heads of the guards.

Down below in the courtyard they saw lots of animals, just like the ones imprisoned in the giant's castle. The young man realised that these, too, had been people once, and that if he failed in his purpose he would become a beast as well.

"Good little horse, now fly up to that tower there."

The winged horse flew him straight to the place he pointed out. The young herdsman jumped down and, magic sword in hand, entered the tower. Lo and behold, in that very spot, swaying to and fro in a rocking chair, sat the terrible witch. Startled, she immediately leapt to her feet.

"Don't move!" ordered the young fellow, who may have been short in stature, but was great in spirit. "Now you will do whatever I command you. For you must surely know that this sword in my hand is the very one which split the enchanted marble."

The witch bowed her head, admitting her defeat.

"I will do whatever you command," she said.

"Well done, that's the idea. So let's go first to re-lease those people down there in the courtyard, that you turned into animals."

They went down at once. The witch lifted the spells from the animals and they turned into people again.

"Now order the guards to open the doors and let the people go."

What choice did she have? She did exactly as the young man told her.

"Now we'll return to the horse," he ordered.

Quickly they ascended to the terrace. The young cowherd set her on the horse's back and mounted up behind her.

"My horse," he commanded, "fly back now to the castle of the wicked giant."

The horse spread its broad wings and soared straight into the sky. But a great journey lay ahead of them. After long hours of flying, they needed a rest to drink water and eat some food.

They landed in a city.

As bad luck would have it, the ruler of this city was a friend of the witch. Pretending to make the young man welcome, he managed secretly to remove the magic sword and hide it. As for the wicked witch, she succeeded in finding another place to conceal herself.

The young man was overcome with grief. Was the lovely maiden now doomed to lie like stone for ever in the castle of the wicked giant? And were the people the terrible witch had turned to animals in that same castle fated to remain imprisoned for ever in its courtyard? No, that must never be! Then he remembered his brothers – but would they realise what desperate need he had of them?

Confronted with this great emergency, however, the mirror in the keeping of the Young Man of the Sea grew cloudy; the penknife given to the Young Man of the Land closed of its own accord; while the cloth kept by the Young Man of the Skies grew red with blood. Thus each of them realised that his brother had great need of him and at once mounted his cloud. And even though they lived far apart from one another, in the end they all assembled in the place they had been summoned to.

"What has happened to you, brother? What evil has befallen you?"

"They have taken my sword, and the witch has escaped from me. If I do not find them both, neither will the marble maiden be released, nor will the wicked giant's animals be restored to human shape again."

Immediately, the Young Man of the Skies begged his father, the Sun, to cast his strong light on the secret hidden corners of the land and sea.

The Young Man of the Land ordered all the animals, including even the ants, to search everywhere for the stolen sword and the missing witch.

And the Young Man of the Sea commanded all the fish to hunt for the sword and the witch in every nook and cranny of the watery kingdom.

Good news soon came. A dolphin brought the cowherd's sword up from the bottom of the sea, while shortly afterwards an ant arrived and revealed the hiding-place of the terrible witch.

So evil had no chance to prosper.

Taking up his sword again, the young man hastened to the spot revealed by the ant and found the witch. He seized her by the hair, threw her across the horse's back, and they flew swiftly to the palace of the wicked giant.

As soon as they arrived and saw the animals, the boy ordered the witch to lift the spells from them.

She had no choice but to undo the magic and they at once turned back into people who, with shouts of joy, thanked the young man who had rescued them.

"And now, forward!" commanded the herdsman, "forward to the chamber where the marble princess lies!"

"You're a fine young man, and I admit you have defeated me," said the witch. "For you I have released so many people, both here and at the Red Tower. So couldn't you do me just one favour in return? Couldn't that maiden who stole the wicked giant's love from me be left to lie in marble for all time?"

"Delay a moment longer, and it will be the end of you!"

What else could the witch do? She accompanied the herdsman to the place where the beautiful princess lay. Stretching out her right hand, with a trembling finger she touched the marble maiden, muttering secret words which she alone had mastery of. And lo and behold, in a little while the maiden's eyes began to flutter.

"It is done," said the witch to the young herdsman. "Now say what other commands you have for me."

"Remove yourself immediately from my sight and be gone for ever." And as the witch vanished, the beautiful princess began to regain consciousness.

She opened her eyes completely and cast them about the room until her gaze fell on the handsome young man. She tried to rise, but did not have the strength. The herdsman took her hand and helped her.

"How long I have slept," she yawned, "and oh! how heavily!"

"That was no sleep. A wicked witch had turned you into marble."

"Her! Oh, I remember her. But I fear she will do me more harm. And if she cannot, then the giant, the wicked giant, will do me more harm still!"

"Fear no more. The wicked giant has been killed."

"And the wicked witch has just this minute drowned in the river," said the herdsman's three brothers, appearing in the doorway.

"But how did I come to be saved?" asked the fair maiden.

As if she already knew the answer, she fixed her large bright eyes on the fine young man, the handsome and noble cowherd who had rescued her. And he, by way of reply, lifted her from the bed in his strong arms and drew her into his embrace. And there and then, in the presence of his brothers, whose faces shone with joy, he planted the kiss of love upon her lips.

The very next day, in that castle which now was theirs by right, a splendid wedding was celebrated, followed by a banquet which lasted nine whole days and nights. The young herdsman's father and mother were there. There also were the princess's royal par-

ents, who thought they had lost their daughter for ever. There, too, were the bridegroom's three new brothers, the fine Young Men of the Land, the Sea and the Skies. There as well were all the people the wicked witch had transformed into animals. And I myself was there – every evening I sat and entertained them with my finest stories.

The servants and the guards rushed to and fro, never quite managing to serve us all, but they were bursting with happiness and high spirits, because they had escaped the clutches of the terrible wicked giant and the even more terrible witch.

> *Mixing lies with what is true*
> *That's what folk-tales always do.*
> *But, though magic has its season,*
> *Give me the man who relies on reason!*

The Bridge at Arta

A score of masons, forty boys, two wagons and a carter,
Three times three hundred days they worked, upon the bridge at Arta.
The whole long day they'd toil away,
But every night it tumbled.
The masons all bewailed their fate,
The apprentices they grumbled:

"Look at our labour, all in vain!
Rivers of sweat we've wasted,
Building the bridge again and again,
To find it devastated!"
Then from the bridge's tumbled arch

A ghostly voice did rumble:
"Seal up a woman in the bridge,
Or its stones will always crumble!
But let it be no orphan child, no passer-by whose losing
Will break no hearts, but let it be a victim of my choosing:
None but the master mason's wife,
She who comes here twice daily
When the sun has risen over the hills
And at nightfall, singing gaily."

The master mason heard the words;
They broke his poor heart, nearly.
He sent a nightingale to say,
(For he loved his young wife dearly)

"Rise late today, and take your time.
Wait till the day is past its prime,
Then dawdle along!"
But the bird heard wrong

... And sang to his wife another song:

184

"Get dressed in haste, comb out your hair,
Come quick, come quick, my lady fair!
Before the sun from its zenith falls,
Make haste to the bridge – your husband calls!"

The mason glimpsed her from afar,
A tiny dot on the dusty track.
He wept and cursed his unlucky star
But knew that he must not send her back.

"Good day to you, builders!" the fair one called,
"But why does my lord look so appalled?"
"Alas, my lady, he's lost his ring,
The one he kept on a golden string.
Into the bridge's arch it fell
And how to recover it none can tell."
"Fear not, good masons," the fair one replied,
Lower me down and I'll crawl inside."

She squeezed through a hole in the base of the arch
And in no time at all completed her search.

"There's no ring down here – I've scoured every inch.
I'm finished – so haul me up on the winch!"

Too late! For already mortar and trowel
And great stones were waiting, the girl to embowel.

Alas!" she cried out, "Our blood must be cursed!
What hope, when the Fates are intent on their worst?
Three sisters condemned to die by their hand,
And all that a tottering bridge might stand!
The first one walled up on the Danube's shore,
The next in Avlona's stony maw,
And now comes my turn, the youngest daughter,
To perish sealed up in the bridge at Arta!
As my heart trembles, so may its walls,
And all travellers fall as my golden hair falls!"

But from deep in the bridge that ghostly voice spoke:
"Change your curse, fair one, lest your words choke
The life from your dear and only brother –
For remember that now you have no other.

What if he chanced to travel this way
And was caught on the bridge as it started to sway?"

So she took back her wish and uttered another,
All on account of her one dear brother:
"Make the bridge hard as ice, as hard as my heart;
Make my hair rods of iron, that its walls may not part!
May travellers cross safely from side to side,
If only I may be satisfied
That my brother, too, may tread without fear
Should ever his journeying bring him here."

187

Born in 1923, Menelaos Stephanides studied economics in Athens, but finally turned from figures to a life of letters. He worked on 'Greek Mythology' for twenty-five years, in cooperation with the artist and illustrator Yannis Stephanides, publishing eighteen volumes of myths for younger readers and a further eight for adults. He then turned his attention from the myths of ancient Greece to stories from more recent times, studying hundreds of traditional Greek folk tales and reworking the most representative of them to show that the Muse which inspired the story-tellers of distant ages worked the same magic for those of later years. Menelaos Stephanides' name is now familiar in many parts of the world, thanks to the translation of both his mythology and the folk tales into several foreign languages. In 1989 his book 'The Argonauts' received the pan-European Pier Paolo Vergerio prize from the University of Padua.

Born in Athens in 1962, Photini Stephanidi, daughter of the painter and illustrator Yannis Stephanides, studied painting and engraving at the Athens School of Fine Art and has since made a name for herself as an engraver and book illustrator. Her published work includes pictures for many children's books and several collectors' editions illustrated with her woodcuts. She has held exhibitions of her paintings and engravings in Greece and abroad. Her work has also been displayed at international book illustration and design exhibitions all over the world.

Prizes: first prize for illustrations by the Greek section of IBBY, Athens 1995; first prize in the Arab World Illustration Biennale, Beirut 1998; Plaque BIB, Bratislava 2001; first prize in Exlibris Trienale, Beograd 2002; State prize for illustration, Athens 2003; Greek nomination for Andersen awards 2004.

If you enjoyed this book and would like others in our range of titles, simply complete the order form below. Prices include post and packaging.

	QUANTITY	×	PRICE	= TOTAL
FOLK TALES FROM GREECE I	....	×	€ 10,00	= ....
FOLK TALES FROM GREECE II	....	×	€ 10,00	= ....
1. THE GODS OF OLYMPUS	....	×	€ 10,00	= ....
2. GODS AND MEN	....	×	€ 10,00	= ....
3. HERACLES	....	×	€ 10,00	= ....
4. THESEUS - PERSEUS	....	×	€ 10,00	= ....
5. JASON AND THE ARGONAUTS	....	×	€ 10,00	= ....
6. THE ILIAD, THE TROJAN WAR	....	×	€ 10,00	= ....
7. THE ODYSSEY	....	×	€ 10,00	= ....
8. OEDIPUS, THE TRAGEDIES	....	×	€ 10,00	= ....
TOTAL	....	×	€ 10,00	= ....

Name: ....

Address: ....

Tel., fax or e-mail: ....

Payment by:

☐ Credit card: Name: ....

   Number: .... Exp. : ....

☐ Bank transfer to the following account:
   IBAN: GR3501101510000015174269413,
   SWIFT (BIC): ETHNGRAA, favor of M. Stephanides

Please mail, fax or e-mail this form to:

SIGMA PUBLICATIONS 20, Mavromihali Street, GR-106 80 Athens
                    fax +30 210 3638941, tel. +30 210 3607667
                    e-mail: sigma@sigmabooks.gr